HEINEMANN GUIDED READERS

STARTER LEVEL

ELEANOR JUPP

Ski Race

HEINEMANN

2

It's Sunday. Sue, Rebecca and their friends arrive at their holiday chalet. Everybody is very excited. They are going to ski. Sue and Rebecca love skiing. They are good at skiing.

It's early on Monday morning. Everybody is at the ski hire shop. Sue and Rebecca are choosing their boots and skis. They put on their boots and carry their skis. Sue has yellow boots and blue skis. Rebecca has red boots and white skis.

Sue's poles are sticking out behind her. Mark trips over Sue's skis.

Are you OK?

Your friend's ski poles are in the way.

You've got big feet!

The snow looks hard.

Yes. The skiing will be fast today.

Sue and Rebecca are in the ski lift.
The hard snow of the piste is below them.
The ski lift is taking them to the top of
the mountain. They are going to ski down
the piste from the top of the mountain.

5

Sue and Rebecca get off the ski lift at the top
of the mountain. Then they ski down the mountain.
They are good skiers. They don't fall over.
David and Mark are watching them.
David and Mark are also good skiers.

The young people ski all day. They enjoy themselves.
In the evening, they ski back to their chalet.
They are very tired.

7

It's Wednesday morning. The young people are waiting to go up on the ski lift.
They are listening to their teacher.
There's going to be a ski race. Sue and Rebecca want to win. David and Mark want to win. Everybody wants to win!

We're arranging a race on Saturday. That's the last day of the holiday. The race is ten kilometres long. It's a long and difficult piste.

I do!

I do!

Who wants to race?

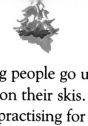

The young people go up the mountain.
They put on their skis. They ski down the piste.
They are practising for the race.
Sue and Rebecca are skiing fast. They want to
win the race. Mark and David are also skiing fast.
They want to pass Sue and Rebecca. But they can't.

Look at them.
They want to win.

But we're going to win.

It's difficult.

Yes.
But it's fun.

It's Saturday morning. Saturday is the last day
of the holiday. It's the day of the race.
The race is in the afternoon. Sue and Rebecca
are hungry. They leave their skis at the side
of the café. They sit down and order lunch.

David and Mark see Sue and Rebecca.
They don't want Sue and Rebecca to win the race.
They find Rebecca and Sue's skis.
They undo a screw on one of Sue's skis.

These are Sue's blue skis.
I'll undo the binding.

Good.
Now the skis won't work.
We're sure to win.

Everybody is ready. The race is starting.
Who is going to win?
Are Sue and Rebecca going to win?
Are David and Mark going to win?

Come on Sue and Rebecca!

Come on David and Mark!

On your marks.
Get set – GO!

Sue and Rebecca are in front. Then Sue's ski comes off. Sue falls. She slides across the snow and off the piste. Rebecca stops to help her. David and Mark ski past. David shouts to Mark.

Ha! Ha!
The screw on her binding is undone.
We're going to win!

Sue and Rebecca repair Sue's ski.
Now Sue can ski again.
They look for the piste.
Suddenly, they see the piste.
They see the other skiers.
Now they are racing again.

Sue and Rebecca come first. They win the race.
It's the end of the holiday.
Back home tomorrow.